ALL JOIN IN

AND OTHER STORIES

Quentin Blake

JONATHAN CAPE
London

ABC

Cockatoos

Clown

Mrs Armitage on Wheels

The Green Ship

This edition first published in the United Kingdom in 2000
by Jonathan Cape Ltd, The Random House Group Ltd
20 Vauxhall Bridge Road, London SW1V 2SA

This edition © 2000 Quentin Blake

All six titles first published by Jonathan Cape
Quentin Blake`s ABC © 1989 Quentin Blake
All Join In © 1990 Quentin Blake
Cockatoos © 1992 Quentin Blake
Clown © 1995 Quentin Blake
Mrs Armitage on Wheels © 1987 Quentin Blake
The Green Ship © 1998 Quentin Blake

ISBN 0224047485

Printed in Singapore by
Tien Wah Press (Pte) Ltd

ABC

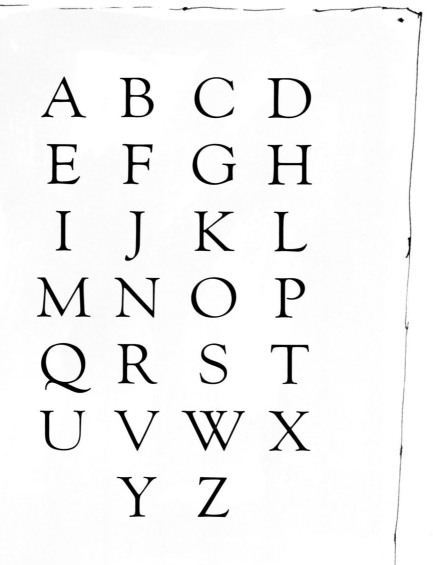

A B C D
E F G H
I J K L
M N O P
Q R S T
U V W X
Y Z

Aa

A is for Apples,
    some green and some red

Bb

B is for Breakfast
we're having in bed

Cc

C is for Cockatoos
learning to scream

Dd

D is for Ducks
upside down in a stream

Ee

E is for Egg
in a nest in a bush

Ff

F is for Firework –
it goes BANG and WHOOSH

Gg

G is for Grandma –
she's really quite fat

Hh

H is for Hair
that goes under your hat.

Ii

I is for Illness
(which *nobody* likes)

Jj

J is for Junk –
rusty beds and old bikes

Kk

K is for Kittens,
    all scratching the chair

Ll

L is for Legs
that we wave in the air

Mm

M is for Mud
that we get on our knees

Nn

N is for Nose –
and he's going to sneeze!

Oo

O is for Ostrich
who gives us a ride

Pp

P is for Parcel –
let's guess what's inside

Qq

Q is for Queen
with a cloak and a crown

Rr

R is for Roller skates –
watch us fall down!

Ss

S is for Sisters,
    some short and some tall

Tt

T is for Tent
where there's room for us all

Uu

U is Umbrella
to keep off the rain

Vv

V is for Vet,
  when your pet has a pain

Ww

W is for Watch –
we can hear the ticktocks

Xx

X is the ending
for jack-in-the-boX

Yy

Y is for Yak –
he's our hairiest friend

Zz

Z is for Zippers,
    That's all
        That's the end

ALL JOIN IN

All Join In

The Hooter Song

Nice Weather for Ducks

Sliding

Sorting Out the Kitchen Pans

Bedtime Song

All Join In

Important Message
YOU CAN JOIN IN
TOO

All Join In

When Sandra plays
the trumpet
it makes a lovely sound

And Mervyn on his
drum-kit
can be heard for
miles around

Stephanie is brilliant
when she plays the violin

But the very best of all is when we

ALL JOIN IN!

When Amy throws a
tantrum
it is wonderful to see

And when Eric starts
his wailing
there is noise enough for three

When Bernard kicks the dustbin
it really makes a din

But the very best of all is when we

ALL JOIN IN!

The Hooter Song

When William's in his study
　　and his thoughts are very deep
We come and help him concentrate –

We go BEEP–BEEP

BEEP–BEEP

When Lilian sings a sad song
  and we think she's going to weep
We like to come and cheer her up –

We go BEEP–BEEP

BEEP–BEEP

When Oscar's on the sofa
    and he's curled up fast asleep
we know he likes a serenade –

We go BEEP–BEEP
BEEP–BEEP

Nice Weather for Ducks

We're all off to the river
   along the muddy track
And we're joining in the Duck Song

  QUACK QUACK QUACK

We each have our umbrella
   and our wellies and our mack
And we're joining in the Duck Song

  QUACK QUACK QUACK

We don't care if it's raining
and the sky is murky black –
We're joining in the Duck Song

QUACK QUACK QUACK

QUACK QUACK

Sliding

It's cold and wet and dark outside
In here we'll have a lovely slide
All down the banisters –

WHEEEE!

It's large and grey and lots of fun
  We're sliding down it one by one
All down the elephant –

WHEEEEE!

We're in the wind and sun and snow
  Let's see how fast our sledge will go
All down the mountainside –

WHEEEEEEE!

BUMP!

Sorting Out the Kitchen Pans

We're sorting out the Kitchen Pans
 DING DONG BANG
Sorting out the Kitchen Pans
 BING BONG CLANG

Sorting out the Kitchen Pans
 TING BANG DONG
Sorting out the Kitchen Pans
 CLANG DING BONG

Sorting out the Kitchen Pans

DONG DANG BONG

TING TANG BING BANG

CLANG DING

OW!

Bedtime Song

The stars above are glittering
The moon is gleaming bright
And noisy cats are singing songs
Down in the yard tonight

MIAOW WOW WOW
WOW WOW

People in their dressing-gowns
In houses far and near
Are leaning from their window sills
They're horrified to hear

MIAOW WOW WOW
WOW WOW

But we don't want
   a lullaby
We prefer a din
Noisy cats are what
   we like –
All join in!

MIAOW WOW WOW
   WOW WOW WOW
      WOW

All Join In

When we're cleaning up the house

We ALL JOIN IN

When we're trying to catch a mouse

We ALL JOIN IN

When we've got some tins of paint

We ALL JOIN IN

And when Granny's going to faint

We ALL JOIN IN

And if Ferdinand decides to make
  a chocolate fudge banana cake
    What do we do? For goodness sake!

We

ALL JOIN IN!

COCKATOOS

Professor Dupont had ten cockatoos.
He was very proud of them.

Every morning he jumped out of bed.

He took a shower and
 he cleaned his teeth,

as he always did.

He got dressed and he tied his tie,
as he always did.

He adjusted his spectacles,
as he always did.

And he went downstairs.

He went into the conservatory.
There were all his cockatoos;
        every single one.

Professor Dupont threw wide his arms.
He said: "Good morning,
        my fine feathered friends!"

Every morning he said the same thing.
The day came when the cockatoos thought they would go
mad if they had to listen to the same words once again.

They decided to have some sport with Professor Dupont.
One after another they escaped through a broken pane of
glass they had discovered in the corner of the conservatory.

Next morning Professor Dupont came into the
conservatory and threw open his arms.
There was not a cockatoo in sight.

Where could all the cockatoos have got to?

Professor Dupont went into the dining-room.
They weren't there.

He went to look in the kitchen.
Hortense the cook was there,
boiling an egg for his breakfast,
but there weren't any cockatoos.

He went to look in the bedroom.
They weren't there.

He looked in the bathroom.
They weren't there.

He looked in the lavatory.
They weren't there.

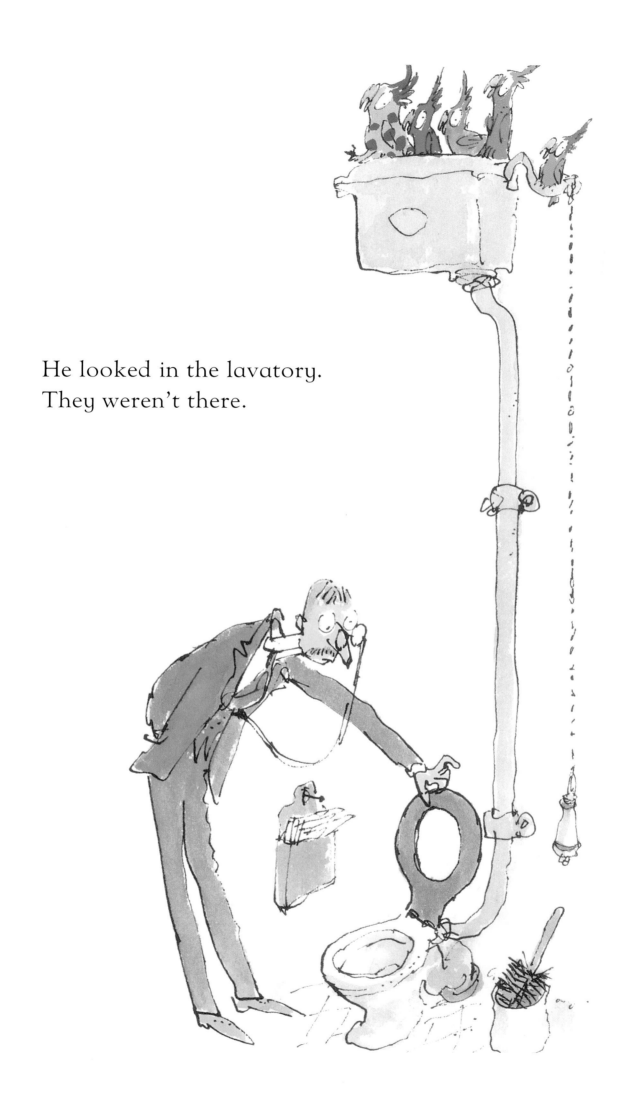

He climbed a ladder
and flashed his torch around the attic.
They weren't there.

He even climbed up to the roof.
But they weren't there.

Professor Dupont went to look in the garage.
His car was there,
but there weren't any cockatoos.

He went down into the cellar; but he couldn't see any cockatoos there, either.

Professor Dupont was at his wit's end.
He couldn't find his cockatoos anywhere.
Where could they possibly have got to?

Professor Dupont spent a restless night.

The next morning he jumped out of bed.
He took a shower and he cleaned his teeth,
as he always did.

He got dressed and he tied his tie,
as he always did.

He adjusted his spectacles,
as he always did.

And he went downstairs.

Professor Dupont went into the conservatory.
There were all his cockatoos, where they
always were – every single one!

Professor Dupont threw wide his arms.
He said: "Good morning,
my fine feathered friends!"

Some people never learn.

CLOWN

127

MRS ARMITAGE
on Wheels

Mrs Armitage was out on her bicycle.
Breakspear the dog ran alongside.

A hedgehog walked across the road.
Tring! Tring! went Mrs Armitage on the bell.

"What this bike needs," said Mrs Armitage to herself,
"is a really loud horn."

Mrs Armitage bought three horns.
They were all very loud.

Beep-beep

Honk-honk

Paheehahurh

went Mrs Armitage on her horns.

Then the chain came off.

By the time Mrs Armitage had got it on again her hands were all black and greasy.

"What this bike needs," said Mrs Armitage to herself,
"is somewhere to wash your hands."

So she got a bucket of water and a towel
and a soap-rack with a bar of soap,
and she hung them all on the bike.
And off she went with
beautifully clean hands.

"What this bike needs," said Mrs Armitage to herself as she cycled along, "if it's to be looked after properly, is a complete tool kit."

So she got a toolbox
with spanners
and screwdrivers
and hammers and
cans of penetrating oil,
and she fixed it
on to the back of the bicycle,
and off she went.

By now Mrs Armitage was beginning to think about food. "What this bike needs," said Mrs Armitage to herself, "is somewhere to carry a light snack."

So she got a tray for apples and bananas and cheese-and-tomato sandwiches, and a holder for a bottle of lemonade and a flask of cocoa, and a special basket for bones and dog biscuits for Breakspear, and she fixed them all to the bike, and off they went.

But by now poor Breakspear was feeling quite tired, running beside the bicycle. You could tell because his tongue was hanging out and he was panting. "What this bike needs," said Mrs Armitage to herself, "is something for a faithful dog to ride on."

So she got some iron brackets and some nuts and bolts and some cushions, and she made a seat for Breakspear, and off they went.

They had stopped beside the road for some sandwiches and dog biscuits when it began to rain. "Great Heavens!" said Mrs Armitage. "What this bike needs, Breakspear, is something to keep the rain off."

So she got two umbrellas, one large, one small, and she fixed them up on the bicycle, and off they went.

Riding through the rain, Mrs Armitage began to feel rather down-hearted. "What this bike needs," said Mrs Armitage to herself, "is a bit of cheerful music."

So she got a transistor radio-cassette player and a lot
of cassettes of cheerful music and a mouth organ so
that she could join in; and fixed them all to the
bike, and off they went.

Mrs Armitage was turning the pedals so fast and
blowing the mouth organ so hard that soon she was
nearly exhausted.
"What this bike needs," said Mrs Armitage to
herself, "is a bit of extra oomph."

And so she got some wood
and some ropes and some
tarpaulin.

She rigged up a mast and a sail and
she added a few yards of bunting
and an anchor into the bargain.

And off they went with the wind behind them,
faster and faster and faster until . . .

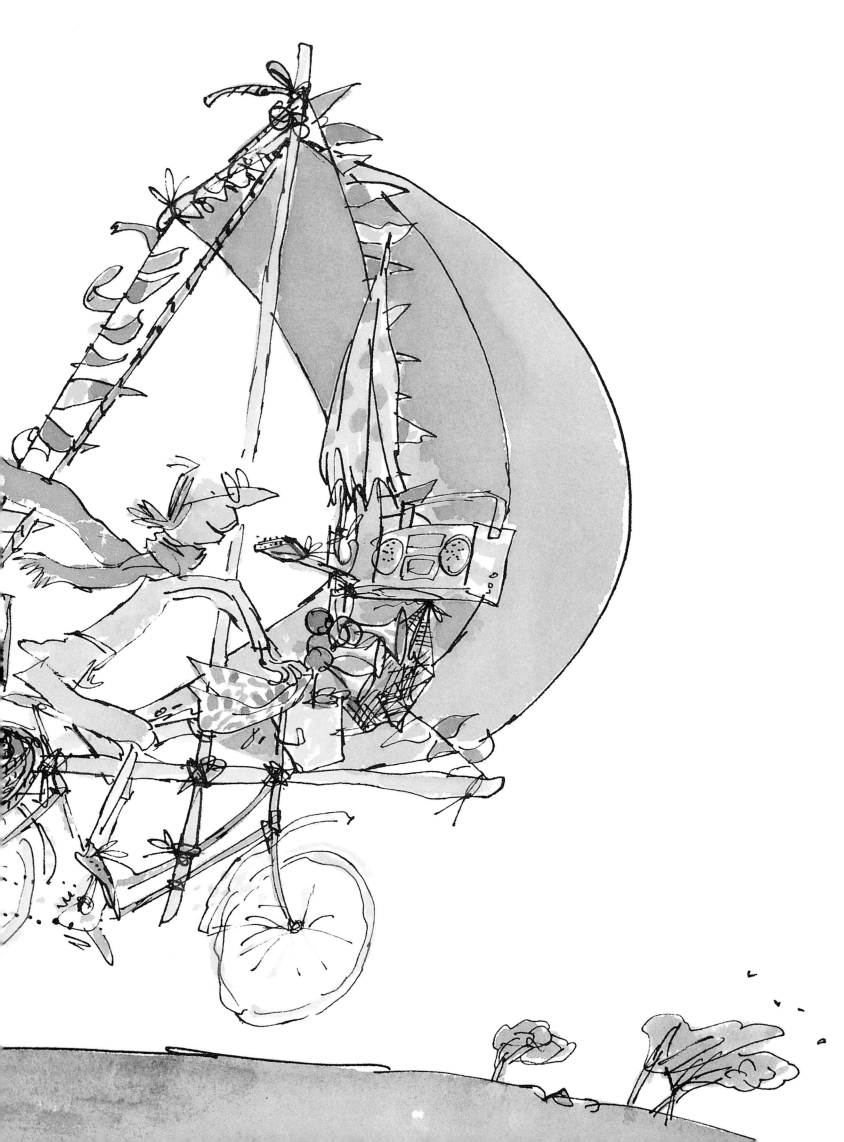

CRASH!

CRUNCH!

CLANG!

CLATTER!

THUD!

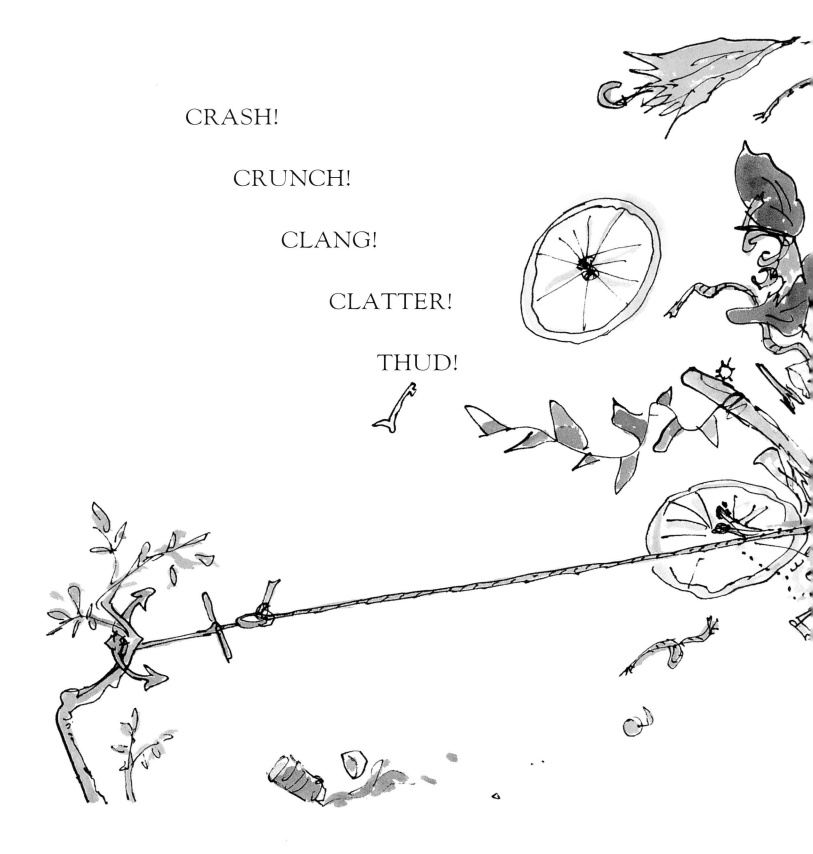

Paheehahurh!

"What this bike needs, Breakspear," said Mrs
Armitage as she picked herself from the wreckage,
"is taking to the dump."

"And what I need is . . ."

"Whoopeeeeeeeeeeeee!"

"But what these roller-skates need,"
said Mrs Armitage to herself,
"what these roller-skates need is . . . ."

The
Green Ship

I can remember very clearly, even now, what it was like when we climbed over the wall into the garden of the big house. We knew we weren't supposed to, but we had been staying with our aunt for a fortnight already, and were beginning to feel bored – so we were on the lookout for an adventure.

Over the wall it wasn't much like the kind of garden we were used to; more like a park, or even a forest.
"We can be explorers," Alice said, crashing into the undergrowth. "I wonder what we shall discover?"
The trees were huge and covered with ivy; it really was very like a jungle.

We plunged deeper and deeper into it. We thought we were completely lost; then all at once we pushed aside a screen of branches and saw something absolutely astonishing.

It was a ship. At least, it wasn't a real ship; but you could see it was meant to be a ship. Bushes had been cut into the shape of the bows and stern, and two trees trimmed to look like funnels. On either side of these there were two tall thin trees with not many branches that were obviously meant to be the masts.
Then Alice said: "Come on. There's nobody about. Let's get a look at it."

Towards the back of the ship there was also something
like a tree house or a small garden shed perched on top
of an ancient tree-stump. A set of wooden steps led up
to it, and we climbed them and went in.

Inside there was a wheel with spokes that stuck out,
just as if it were a proper ship. On the little shelf there
was a telescope, and next to it a photo in a brown
wooden frame of a man in uniform. From the roof
hung an old lantern. Through the windows you could
see for miles. You could almost believe you were at sea.

And then suddenly we were taken by surprise by a
voice which said: "Well, what have we here, Bosun?
Stowaways?"

There was a thin lady in a dark dress looking up at us.
"What do you think, Bosun? Shall we clap them in
irons?"
"Only youngsters," said the Bosun, who actually
looked more like a gardener.
"Swabbin' the decks is the thing, if you ask me."
"And after that perhaps we shall have tea on deck."

Swabbing the decks turned out to be sweeping away the leaves; but tea really was tea, with madeira cake and cucumber sandwiches. At the end of it Mrs Tredegar (that was her name) said: "The Bosun will see you ashore. And why not come aboard again tomorrow? I'm sure that's what the Captain would have wished."

Next morning, with permission
from our aunt, we were back at
the green ship.

We climbed the masts.

We took turns to stand at
the wheel and steer the ship.

Mrs Tredegar showed us how
to use the telescope.

By the end of the day we
were a fully-trained crew.

On our next visit Mrs Tredegar produced an old atlas, and every day after that we imagined that we were voyaging to some new place.

A flower urn became an Italian ruin;

a palm tree (there really was a palm tree) became the far-off shore of Egypt.

One chilly day we pretended we were in the Arctic. Bushes became icebergs and some sheep that had got into the garden by mistake became polar bears.

The last few days of our holiday were hot and sunny.
They got hotter and hotter. We wore sun hats and played
deck-quoits and drank lots of limejuice. It
seemed as though we were heading southward through
tropical seas.

Eventually it became so hot that Mrs Tredegar decided that we must have reached the Equator, and that we must have the ceremony of Crossing the Line. The Bosun was King Neptune, with a beard made of garden twine and a hayfork for a trident.

First-timers had to be shaved; which seemed to include
Alice as well as me. There was a bucket of soapsuds
and a sort of wooden butterknife from the kitchen, and
we all got very wet.

The next day was the last full day of our holiday and it
was agreed that we should stay overnight at the big
house. The weather was hotter than ever and
everything was absolutely still. And then, after tea, the
sky suddenly turned a strange colour and large drops
of rain began to fall. "There's going to be a storm,"
said Mrs Tredegar. "Come on, crew, into the wheelhouse."

A huge warm wind blew through the garden.
Mrs Tredegar took the wheel.
"What would the captain have done?" she said.
"Steer into the eye of the storm. That's it.
Steer into the eye of the storm."

And what a storm it was!
There were huge claps of thunder; lightning
crackled across the whole of the sky.

The swaying of the lantern and the rain rushing against the windows made it seem as though we were truly at sea. And the storm seemed to go on for ever.

At some point we must have fallen asleep, because when we awoke we were on the floor of the wheelhouse and early morning sunlight was shining on us.

Mrs Tredegar was still at the wheel.

"She came through," she said. "She came through."

Then she turned and looked at us and said: "Well done, crew. The captain would have been proud of you."

And then Mrs Tredegar walked out across the grass
and with a long tail of ivy tied up the battered ship
as if she had come into port at last.

We still go back to see Mrs Tredegar every year. The Bosun says that he's getting too stiff to climb up and trim the masts and the funnels; and that Mrs Tredegar doesn't seem to mind.

And so gradually, year by year, the trees are growing back into their old shape; they are becoming ordinary trees, and soon there will no longer be any way at all of knowing that they were once the Green Ship.